D0537617

# The Signalman
## *and*
# The Ghost at the Trial

Retold by F. H. Cornish

**MACMILLAN**

*Founding Editor:* John Milne

The Macmillan Readers provide a choice of enjoyable reading materials for learners of English. The series is published at six levels – Starter, Beginner, Elementary, Pre-intermediate, Intermediate and Upper.

### Level control
Information, structure and vocabulary are controlled to suit the students' ability at each level.

### The number of words at each level:

| | |
|---|---|
| Starter | about 300 basic words |
| Beginner | about 600 basic words |
| Elementary | about 1100 basic words |
| Pre-intermediate | about 1400 basic words |
| Intermediate | about 1600 basic words |
| Upper | about 2200 basic words |

### Vocabulary
Some difficult words and phrases in this book are important for understanding the story. Some of these words are explained in the story and some are shown in the pictures. From Pre-intermediate level upwards, words are marked with a number like this: ...³. These words are explained in the Glossary at the end of the book.

# Contents

A Map of London in the 1860s

# A Note About the Author

**Charles Dickens** was born on 7th February 1812. The Dickens family lived near Portsmouth, on the south coast of England. Later, the family lived in London. Dickens had three brothers and three sisters. Dickens' father, John, was a clerk in an office. He worked for the British Navy. But John did not spend his money carefully. He owed people money. In 1824, he was sent to a prison.

Dickens' father, mother, brothers and sisters all lived in the prison. Dickens had to work in a factory. He never forgot this difficult time.

Dickens went to school for only a few years. But he read many books and he educated himself. In 1834, Dickens became a newspaper reporter. He also began to write stories. His first stories were printed in magazines. These stories were very, very popular. Dickens became the most famous English writer in the nineteenth century.

In 1836, Dickens married Catherine Hogarth. They had ten children. But Catherine and Charles were not happy. In 1857, Dickens met an actress, Ellen Ternan. He fell in love with her. Dickens separated from his wife in 1858.

Dickens worked hard all his life. He became very rich. Dickens travelled in England, Scotland, Ireland and America. He read his stories in theatres. At this time, ghost stories were very popular. Everybody loved Dickens' ghost stories.

Some of Charles Dickens' stories are: *Oliver Twist* (1837–1839), *Bleak House* (1852–1853), *A Tale of Two Cities* (1859), *Great Expectations* (1860–1861), *A Christmas Carol* (1843) and *Our Mutual Friend* (1864–1865).

Dickens died on 8th June 1870. He was 58 years old. He was buried in the famous church, Westminster Abbey, in London.

# A Note About These Stories

**Time**: 1861. **Places**: London and the south-east of England.

The two stories in this book are ghost stories. *The Signalman* is about a railway. The story was written in 1866.

There were no cars at this time. In towns, people travelled in coaches or carriages or omnibuses. All these were pulled by horses. But people could travel between towns and cities on railway trains.

a carriage      a coach      an omnibus

People first travelled on railway trains in 1825. This happened in Britain. From the 1830s to the 1860s, many railway lines were built in Britain. The lines were metal tracks. People could go on long journeys by railway. And they could travel quickly. A train had several carriages. These carriages were joined together. People sat on seats in the railway carriages. A train carried many people.

The trains travelled along the metal tracks. But the trains could not travel up hills and mountains. There were long tunnels through large hills and mountains. The railway trains travelled on the metal tracks through these tunnels. The ground of small hills was cut away. The railway track was on the flat ground, at the bottom of these cuttings.

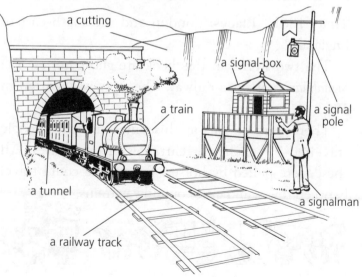

a cutting

a signal-box

a train

a signal pole

a tunnel

a signalman

a railway track

The first railways were very dangerous. There were

many accidents on the railway lines. Then signalmen made the railways safer. Signalmen used special machines. These were called telegraph machines. These telegraph machines sent messages about trains. The messages were sent by electricity.

Signalmen worked in signal-boxes – special buildings near the railway tracks. There was a signal-box at every railway station. And there was a signal-box at each end of every tunnel. Signalmen watched the trains carefully. They sent messages to each other – messages about the trains.

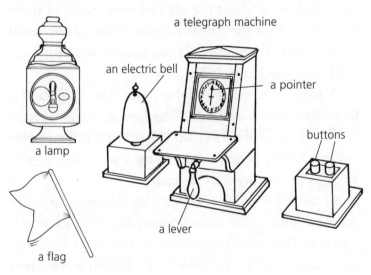

a telegraph machine

an electric bell

a pointer

buttons

a lamp

a lever

a flag

The story, *The Ghost at the Trial*, was first called 'A Trial for Murder'. Dickens wrote the story in 1865. The story is about a trial in a famous law court in London – the Old Bailey. The Old Bailey is a large building. There are many courtrooms in the building.

7

In this story, there is going to be a trial for murder. The police have arrested a man. The man is accused of murdering his friend. In the court, the accused man will be asked many questions.

A lawyer for the prosecution will ask the accused man questions. This lawyer will say, 'This man is Guilty. He is guilty of murder.' A lawyer for the defence will also ask the accused man questions. This lawyer will say, 'This man is Not Guilty. He did not murder his friend.'

Many people will come into the court. Some of them will speak about the accused man. Some of them will speak about the murdered man. Some of them will speak about the murder. These people are witnesses. And their words are evidence.

A judge is in charge of the court. The judge and a jury listen to the evidence. The jury makes a decision about the accused person – Is the person Guilty or Not Guilty? Twelve people are in a jury. One of them – the foreman of the jury – is the leader.

At the time of this story, judges, lawyers and the people in juries were men. Women did not work in the courts in Britain. Murderers were hanged. A rope was put around a guilty person's neck. The rope was then pulled tight and the person died.

In this story, people travel in hansom cabs. These were small carriages pulled by one horse. These carriages were taxis.

a hansom cab

# THE SIGNALMAN

## 1

## The Railway Cutting

It was nine o'clock on a warm summer evening. I stood at the top of a steep slope. The slope was one side of a railway cutting. I looked down. The cutting was very deep. There were two railway tracks at the bottom of the cutting.

I looked to the right – towards London. The railway tracks disappeared into a tunnel. It was a long tunnel through a large hill. The entrance to the tunnel was very dark.

Then I looked to the left – towards Dover. The railway tracks were straight for many miles. I did not see any trains on the tracks.

I looked down into the cutting again.

There was a signal-box at the bottom of the cutting. The signal-box was a small wooden building. It's floor was four feet above the ground. The signal-box was next to the railway tracks. And it was fifty feet from the entrance to the tunnel.

A signalman was standing by the metal tracks. He was standing outside the signal-box. He was holding a red flag. The flag was a piece of red cloth on a long wooden handle.

There was another flag on a tall metal pole near the tunnel entrance. That flag was white. There were also two lamps on the ground, near the pole. The lamps were not lit. A metal ladder was fixed to the pole.

The signalman walked to the pole and he lit one of the lamps. He climbed the ladder and he took the white flag from the pole. Then he put the red flag on the pole and he put the lamp under the flag. The light from the lamp was red.

The signalman climbed down the ladder and he lit the other lamp. The light from this lamp was white. The man held up the lamp and he looked around. Then he started to walk back to the signal-box.

I shouted down to him.

The signalman heard my voice but he did not look up at me. He turned round and he looked towards the tunnel. I was surprised. I was above him, at the top of the cutting. Why was the signalman looking towards the tunnel?

The man turned round again, and I saw his face. He was frightened! Why was the signalman frightened?

I shouted again. 'Hello! Hello!'

At last, the signalman looked up at me.

'I want to talk to you!' I shouted. 'Is there a path into this cutting?'

The signalman looked at me, but he did not reply.

Suddenly, the ground started to shake. There was a loud noise and a big train came out of the tunnel. Clouds of white smoke came up from the cutting. Then the smoke disappeared and I saw the train again. It was far away. It was going to Dover.

The signalman was walking towards the tunnel.

I shouted my question again. 'Hello! Hello! Is there a path into this cutting?'

The signalman stopped and he looked at me. Then he lifted his white flag. He pointed to my left.

I looked to the left. About three hundred feet away, there was a path.

'Thank you!' I shouted.

The path was very steep. The ground was very wet and muddy. I walked carefully down into the cutting. Once, I stopped and I looked at the signalman. He was standing by one of the railway tracks. He was watching me. He was watching and waiting. He was unhappy. Why?

I arrived at the bottom of the cutting. I walked beside the metal track. I walked towards the signalman.

There were walls of earth on both sides of the cutting. The walls were very high and they were dark and wet. Water was running down the walls. I looked up and I saw a small piece of sky. The sky was orange and red. The sun was going down at the end of the day. But the sun was not shining into the cutting.

In front of me was the dark entrance to the long tunnel. A cold wind was blowing through the tunnel. The wind had a cold, dead smell. Suddenly, I was cold. I was very cold!

Soon, I was standing beside the signalman. The man had dark hair and a pale face. His beard and eyebrows were thick and black.

'Good evening,' I said to the signalman. 'You work in a lonely place. Do you like visitors?'

The man did not reply. I smiled at him.

'I will tell you about myself,' I said. 'I worked in an office for thirty years. Now, I have retired from work. I don't do any work now.'

The man did not reply.

'I'm very interested in railways,' I said. 'I was a boy sixty years ago. There were no trains then, and there were no railway tracks. Now, I'm travelling around England. I'm visiting railways. I want to see the great trains. And I want to see the long tunnels and the great bridges. Men can make wonderful things in this nineteenth century!'

The signalman did not speak to me. He was looking at the entrance to the tunnel. And he was looking at the red light next to the entrance. Was he waiting for somebody?

'Do you take care of the flags and the lights?' I asked the man. It was his job. I knew that. But I wanted the man to speak.

'Yes, I take care of the flags and lights,' he replied quietly. 'They are the signals.'

'Tell me about the signals,' I said.

The signalman pointed to the railway track near his feet.

'This is the Up Line – the track to London,' he said. Then he pointed to the other track. 'And that is the Down Line – the track to Dover.'

'Sometimes, a train to London has to wait here,' he said. 'Sometimes, there is a train on the Down Line, at the other end of the tunnel. The London train waits here by the signal pole. The Dover train comes through the tunnel. Then the London train goes on again. Two trains must not be in the tunnel at the same time, sir.'

'Tell me more about your signals,' I said.

'I stop trains with a red signal,' said the signalman. 'A red signal is a warning signal. In the day-time, the train driver sees my red flag on the pole. He stops his

14

train. At night-time, the driver sees my red lamp on the pole. He stops the train. The white flag and the white light tell the driver – GO THROUGH THE TUNNEL. The driver sees the white flag or the white light and he does not stop his train.'

'I understand,' I said. 'The flags are your day-time signals and the lamps are your night-time signals.'

'Yes, sir,' the man said. 'That is correct.'

The signalman's face was pale. His eyes did not move.

A strange thought came into my mind. 'I am talking to a dead man!' I thought.

Then another thought came into my mind. 'This man is frightened of me!' I thought. 'Why?'

'You are worried!' I said. I smiled at the signalman. 'Have I frightened you?'

'I was worried,' he replied. 'Have I seen you before? Have I seen you *there*?'

He pointed to the signal pole by the tunnel entrance. I looked at the pole and the red light.

'Dear sir, I have never stood there,' I said. 'I have never been in this rail-way cutting before.'

He looked at me carefully. Then he replied. 'No. No, you haven't been here before, sir.'

Suddenly, the signalman was happier. 'Come into the signal-box, sir,' he said. 'It's cold here.'

I followed him along the railway track. We went up some wooden stairs into the signal-box.

# 2

## In the Signal-box

'Please sit down, sir,' the signalman said.

A fire was burning in the fireplace and the small room was warm. I looked around the room. There were two chairs and a desk. I sat in one of the chairs.

On the desk, there was an electric bell. There was also a telegraph machine. I am very interested in telegraph machines. Telegraph machines bring messages and they send messages.

A telegraph machine has a clock-face. But there are letters on the face, not numbers. A clock has two pointers on its face. They point to the numbers on the face. Somebody can look at the face and read the time. But there is only one pointer on a telegraph machine. It points to the letters on the face. Somebody can read the letters. The letters make a message.

'Tell me about your electric bell and your telegraph machine,' I said to the man. 'Who sends messages to you? Who receives messages from you?'

'Electric wires go from the bell and the telegraph in this signal-box,' the signalman replied. 'Some wires go to the bell and the telegraph in the signal-box at the other end of the tunnel. Some wires go to the signal-box at the next station.' He pointed towards Dover.

'I can receive messages from both those signal-boxes,' he said. 'And I can send messages to them. I can send and receive bell messages. And I can send and receive telegraph messages.'

'What bell messages do you receive?' I asked.

'The bell rings once,' the signalman said. 'That means – THERE IS A MESSAGE FOR YOU. Sometimes I am outside the signal-box. I hear the bell and I come in. I wait for a message. The bell messages are simple.'

'Sometimes, the bell rings once, then it rings twice,' the signalman said. 'The signalman at the station is saying – THERE IS A TRAIN ON THE UP LINE. IT HAS PASSED MY SIGNAL BOX. SOON, IT WILL ARRIVE AT YOUR SIGNAL BOX. Then I put a signal on the pole – a white signal. That means – GO THROUGH THE TUNNEL.'

'Sometimes, the bell rings once, then it rings three times,' he said. 'The man in the signal-box at the other end of the tunnel is saying – THERE IS A TRAIN ON THE DOWN LINE. SOON, IT WILL COME THROUGH THE TUNNEL. STOP ALL OTHER TRAINS AT YOUR SIGNAL-BOX. Then I put my red warning signal on the pole. I put the red flag or the red lamp on the pole. Do you understand?'

'Yes,' I said. 'I understand.'

'I send bell messages too,' the signalman said. 'A train passes my signal-box, going to Dover. I press this button.'

He pointed to a button near the bell.

'The bell rings in the signal-box at the station. The man in that box waits for a message. Then I press the button three times. That tells him about the train.'

'Or I press *this* button,' the man said. He pointed to another button.

'The bell rings in the signal-box at the other end of the tunnel. I press the button once. Then I press it twice. That tells the signalman in *that* signal-box about the train.'

'And the telegraph machine?' I said. 'What are the telegraph messages?'

'I can send longer messages with that machine,' the signalman said.

'I ring the bell in one of the signal-boxes once, then six times,' he said. 'The signalman there waits for a message on his telegraph machine. I move the pointer on my machine to a letter. Then I press this lever.'

He showed me a lever below the clock-face.

'The pointer in the other signal-box moves to the same letter. Then I send the next letter of the message, then the next.'

'The other signalmen can send me messages too,' the man said. 'The bell here rings once, then it rings six times. I watch my telegraph machine. I write down the letters, then I can read the message.'

'You have an interesting job,' I said. 'But it is dark and lonely here in this cutting. Do you often walk up to the top?'

The signalman started to reply. 'The electric bell —'

Suddenly, the bell on the desk rang once. Then the bell rang six times. The signalman wrote a message on a piece of paper – a message from the telegraph machine. Quickly, he sent a reply.

'I have to be near the bell,' the signalman said. 'I do not go far from the signal-box.'

The bell rang again. The signalman stopped talking again. Another message came and the man replied to it.

'Do you like your job?' I asked. 'It *is* very lonely here.'

'It is a good job for me, sir,' he replied. 'Many years ago, I was a student —'

The signalman stopped talking. He looked at the electric bell. But it had not rung! He went to the door and he opened it. He looked along the track towards the red light. Then he closed the door and he sat down. Suddenly he was frightened again.

'I was a student,' he said again. 'But I was not a good student. I could not get an important job —'

Again, he turned and he looked at the electric bell. But the bell had not rung!

The man spoke again.

'Now I do this job,' he said. 'I do the job well. Sometimes I work all day. Sometimes I work all night. It's quiet here. I read books and I study too. I have learnt the French language. And I have learnt some mathematics.'

'You are a happy man!' I said.

But he was not a happy man. He was very unhappy. Why was he unhappy and frightened?

'I am not a happy man, sir,' he said very quietly. 'Once, I was happy. Now I am very worried.'

'Why are you worried?' I asked.

'It is late, sir,' the signalman replied. 'Will you visit me again? We will talk again another day.'

'Yes, I will come again,' I said. 'I am staying at a hotel, one mile from here. When shall I come?'

'Come tomorrow, sir,' he replied. 'I start my work at ten o'clock in the evening.'

'I will come at eleven o'clock,' I said. 'Now, I must go.' I stood up.

'Tell me, sir,' the man said. 'Why did you shout, "Hello! Hello!" this evening?'

'I was shouting to you,' I replied. 'I wanted to talk to you.'

'Did you hear a voice?' the signalman asked. 'Did a voice in your mind say those words?'

'No,' I replied. 'Why do you ask that question?'

He did not answer me.

'Good night, sir,' he said. 'Go quickly now. I will hold up my white light. You will see the path. Please don't shout to me tomorrow.'

# 3

# The Figure by the Tunnel

The next night, at eleven o'clock, I was walking down the path. The signalman was waiting for me at the bottom of the cutting. He was holding up his white light.

We walked to the signal-box and we went up the stairs. We went inside the signal-box and the signalman closed the door. We sat next to the fire.

'I will tell you my story now,' he said very quietly. 'Yesterday I saw *you* – I know that. You are not *him*!'

'Yesterday, I came here for the first time,' I said. 'Who are you talking about?'

'I don't know,' said the signalman. 'I have never seen his face. Sometimes he puts his hands in front of his face. And sometimes he holds his left arm in front of his face and he waves his right arm. He does *this*!'

The signalman put his left arm in front of his face. He moved his right arm from side to side.

'Frightened people wave their arms,' I thought.

Then I had another thought. 'Frightened people wave their arms and they shout. They shout, "Get out of the way! Please, please, get out of the way!" Yes, the signalman has seen a frightened person!'

'I will tell you my story from the beginning,' said the signalman. 'Please listen to me!'

'One night, a year ago,' he said, 'I was sitting here. I heard a voice. The voice shouted, "Hello! Hello!"'

'I got up and I opened the door,' said the signalman. 'Then, I saw somebody. A figure was standing near the tunnel. He was standing by the red warning light. He was waving his arm. He shouted, "Danger! Danger!" I heard those words.'

'I picked up my white light, sir,' the signalman said. 'I ran towards the figure. "What is wrong?" I shouted. The figure put his arm in front of his eyes and he did not look at me. I was going to touch his arm. But suddenly, the figure disappeared!'

'Did the figure go into the tunnel?' I asked.

'No,' he replied. 'I ran into the tunnel. I ran a long way. But I did not see the figure. The tunnel was dark and cold and wet. I was frightened. I had left my bell and my signals. I ran out of the tunnel very fast.'

I listened to the signalman. He spoke quietly.

'I came back to the signal-box,' he said. 'Then, I telegraphed to the signalman at the station. And I telegraphed to the signalman at the other end of the tunnel. My message was, I RECEIVED A DANGER WARNING. IS ANYTHING WRONG? I was very worried, sir. But both signalmen replied, THERE IS NOTHING WRONG.'

'But there *was* something wrong,' the signalman said. 'It was a terrible night, sir!'

Suddenly, my body shook. I was cold and I was frightened. I did not want to listen. But I liked the signalman and I wanted to help him.

'Everybody sees strange things,' I said. 'And everybody hears strange things too. Listen to the wind! The cutting is deep and the tunnel is long. The wind in the tunnel makes strange noises. The wind in this cutting makes noises too.'

'Sir,' said the signalman quietly, 'I have not finished my story.'

'I'm sorry,' I said. 'Please tell me more.'

The signalman touched my arm.

'Sir,' he said. 'I saw that figure near the warning light. Six hours later, there was a terrible accident in the tunnel. The next morning, men were carrying dead people and dying people out of the tunnel.'

This was a terrible story. But I tried to help the unhappy signalman again.

'Many strange things happen,' I said. 'And we do not know —'

'Excuse me, sir,' said the signalman quickly. 'I have not finished my story.'

'I'm sorry,' I said again. 'Please tell me more.'

'That accident happened a year ago,' the signalman said. 'I could not sleep after the accident. I could not eat. I was ill. Then, after three months, I was happier. But six months ago, I saw the figure again.'

'Tell me about that,' I said.

'Sir,' the man said. 'I was standing at the door here.' He pointed at it. 'It was early in the morning. The sun was shining into the cutting. I looked towards the dark tunnel. And there was the figure!'

We were both silent for a moment.

'Did he shout to you?' I asked.

'No, he was silent,' the signalman replied.

'Did he wave his arm?' I asked.

'No, sir,' said the signalman. 'He stood in the sun-light and he put both his hands in front of his face.'

The signalman put his hands in front of his face. He

covered his eyes. 'He did *this*, sir,' he said.

I watched the signalman. My body shook again.

'I have seen figures with their hands in front of their faces,' I thought. 'I have seen them on graves! They are stone figures in graveyards. The stone figures are crying. Has the signalman seen somebody crying near the tunnel?'

'Did you run towards the tunnel?' I asked the signalman.

'No. I sat down,' he replied. 'I was ill. After a few minutes, I looked towards the tunnel again. The figure had gone.'

'What happened next?' I asked.

The signalman touched my arm again.

'Sir, later that day, a Dover train came out of the tunnel,' he said. 'The people in the last carriage were waving their arms. The train driver was looking back. I waved a flag and he saw me. The train went five hundred feet past the signal-box. Then it stopped. I ran along the track to the train.'

'A beautiful young lady had died in the last carriage, sir,' the signalman said. 'We carried her body along the track. We brought her body into the signal-box.'

We were both silent for a minute. The wind made strange noises outside.

'The young woman died six months ago,' the signalman said at last. 'Last week, the figure came back. He is a ghost, sir. I know that now. I have seen the ghost many times this week.'

'You have seen the figure again?' I said.

'Yes,' he replied. 'I've seen him near the red light.

The light is a warning. The ghost is a warning too!'

'What does the figure do now?' I asked.

'He does this, sir,' the man said. 'He waves.'

The signalman put his left arm in front of his face again. He waved his right arm from side to side.

Again I thought, 'Frightened people wave their arms like that. And they shout, "Get out of the way! Please, please, get out of the way!" Is the ghost frightened? *Is* there a ghost? Is the signalman mad?'

'The ghost comes every day now,' said the signalman. 'Sometimes he shouts to me for many minutes. "Hello! Hello! Danger! Danger!" he shouts. He waves to me. He rings my electric bell. He is giving me a warning!'

'Did he ring your bell yesterday evening?' I asked.

'Yes, sir. He rang it twice,' said the signalman. 'You were here, sir.'

'The bell rang twice and you took two messages,' I said. 'You replied to them. The bell did *not* ring again.'

'The ghost rang the bell,' replied the signalman. '*You* did not hear it, but *I* heard it. The ghost rings the bell very quietly.'

'And did the ghost shout to you last night?' I asked.

'Yes,' he replied. 'I opened the door and he was there. He *was* there!'

'Come to the door with me now,' I said. 'Let's look for the figure now.'

The frightened signalman opened the door. The wind was cold. The walls of the cutting were dark and

29

wet. I saw the red light by the tunnel.

'Do you see the figure?' I asked.

'No,' he replied. 'He isn't there now.'

'No,' I said. 'The figure isn't there.'

He closed the door again and we sat down.

'There is no ghost. I know that,' I thought. 'But this man sees a ghost. He is ill. I want to help him. '

'I want to know something,' the signalman said. 'What is the ghost's warning about?'

I did not reply. I wanted to say, 'There is no ghost.' But I said nothing.

The signalman hit his head with his hand. 'What can I do?' he said. 'Shall I send a telegraph message?'

'Yes,' I said. 'Send the message – THERE IS DANGER! BE VERY CAREFUL.'

'The other signalmen will answer, sir,' the man said. 'They will answer – WHAT DANGER? WHERE IS THE DANGER? Then I will reply – I DON'T KNOW. BUT THERE IS DANGER! And they will send the message – YOU ARE MAD!'

'Then I will not have a job, sir,' the signalman said. He hit his head with his hand again. He was very unhappy.

'The ghost has given me a warning,' he said quietly. 'A terrible thing is going to happen. What can I do?'

I did not say, 'There is no ghost.' I tried to help the signalman.

'You have an important job,' I said. 'You must do your job well. But you are tired and unhappy. You must have a holiday.'

The signalman was silent and he looked at me for a long time.

'You are right,' he said at last. 'Yes, I must do my job well.'

He got up and he went to his desk. He looked at the telegraph machine.

'Shall I stay here with you tonight?' I asked.

'No, sir,' he replied. 'Do not stay. You have been very kind to me. You have listened to my story. And you have helped me. But go back to your hotel now.'

I left the signal-box at two o'clock in the morning. I looked at the dark entrance to the tunnel and the red light. I looked at the wet walls of the high railway cutting. I looked back at the small wooden signal-box. I was cold and frightened. I walked up the path.

'That man is very unhappy,' I thought. 'He is ill. I must help him. I will take him to a doctor. I will come back tomorrow evening and I will talk to the signal-man again.'

# 4

# The Last Accident

The next day was sunny and warm. In the early evening, I walked towards the railway cutting. The sun was shining.

I walked to the top of the cutting.

'I stood here two days ago,' I thought. 'I stood on this slope and I looked down into the cutting.'

Again, I looked down towards the tunnel. I saw a figure. He was near the entrance to the tunnel. His left arm was in front of his face. He was waving his right arm from side to side!

It was horrible! Suddenly, I was cold. My body shook. There *was* a ghost! I closed my eyes.

Then I opened my eyes and I looked again. No, the figure was not a ghost. It was a man. And another man was watching him.

The red warning light was not lit. The entrance to the tunnel was dark. Near the signal pole, there was a tent – a small green tent.

'What has happened?' I thought. 'What is wrong?'

I ran down the path to the bottom of the cutting. I ran to the men near the tunnel.

'What has happened?' I asked them.

The man by the tunnel entrance stopped waving his arm.

'A train killed a signalman here this afternoon, sir,' the other man said. The man was short and thin. He was wearing a dark coat and a tall hat.

'Was it the signalman from this signal-box?' I asked. I pointed at the small wooden building behind me.

'Yes, sir,' the short, thin man said.

'Oh no!' I said.

'Did you know him, sir?' asked the man.

'Yes,' I said quietly. 'He was a good signalman.'

The man lifted the side of the small tent. I looked down at the pale, dead face of the signalman.

'Yes, I knew that signalman,' I said. 'What happened to him? What happened?'

'A train hit him, sir,' the man said. 'He did his job well. But he was on the railway track. The accident happened this afternoon. The signalman put the red flag on the pole. It was a warning for the London train. But then he stood on the track, on the Down Line. Why did he do that, sir?'

'I don't know,' I said. 'What happened next?'

'A train came through the tunnel,' the man said. 'The train hit the signalman.'

'This is the train driver, sir,' he said. He pointed to the man by the signal pole. 'Tom, tell this gentleman your story.'

'I saw you from the top of the cutting,' I said to Tom. 'You were waving your arm.'

'Yes, sir,' he replied. 'I was telling this man about the accident.'

'Please tell *me* about it,' I said.

'I was driving my train through the tunnel,' Tom said. 'I saw the daylight at the end of the tunnel. Then I saw the signalman on the track. He was staring at the signal pole. The train was going very fast. I tried to stop the train. There is a loud bell on the train, sir. I rang the bell, but the signalman did not hear it. He started walking along the track. I shouted to him. I shouted very loudly.'

'What did you shout?' I asked.

'I shouted, "Hello! Hello! Danger! Danger! Get out

34

of the way! Please, please, get out of the way!" Tom said. 'But the signalman did not hear me, sir. And he did not hear the train!'

My body shook. I was cold and frightened.

'Oh, sir!' said the train driver. 'It was terrible. I shouted and shouted but the signalman did not hear me. I could not look at him. I put one arm in front of my face. I waved my other arm from side to side. I did *this* sir. But he did not see me.'

I said goodbye to the two men. Sadly, I left the railway cutting.

I was thinking about the train driver's words. I had heard those words before!

I had shouted, 'Hello! Hello!' to the signalman. I had shouted to him on my first visit to his signal-box.

The ghost had shouted, 'Danger! Danger!' to the signalman.

And I had said the words, 'Get out of the way! Please, please, get out of the way!'

But no! I had not said those words. I had thought the words in my mind!

I remembered my second visit to the signalman. He had talked about the ghost. These were his words –

*He holds his left arm in front of his face. He waves his right arm from side to side.*

And I remembered my thoughts that night.

These were my thoughts –

*Frightened people wave their arms and they shout. They shout, 'Get out of the way! Please, please, get out of the way!'*

I had not said those words. I had thought them. They were words in my mind.

And today, the train driver had shouted some of those words – the words from my own mind.

The end of this story was as strange as its beginning.

# THE GHOST AT THE TRIAL

## 1

## Piccadilly

My name is George Fotherley.
I have an important job in a
famous bank in London. I
work in London and I live in
London too. I live in a large
apartment on the third floor
of a large building. The building is in a famous street. The
street is called Piccadilly.

There are seven rooms in
my apartment. Three of them

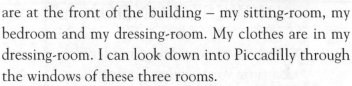

are at the front of the building – my sitting-room, my
bedroom and my dressing-room. My clothes are in my
dressing-room. I can look down into Piccadilly through
the windows of these three rooms.

The other four rooms are at the back of the building
– the dining-room, the kitchen, the bathroom and the
servants' bedroom.

There is a narrow corridor between the rooms at the
front of the apartment and the rooms at the back.

Soon, I will tell you my story. But first, I must tell
you about myself.

I am a lonely man. I am not married. My servant, John Derrick, and his wife live with me. They take care of me. I do not know many people. But I see many people. Often, I look out of the window of my sitting-room. There are always people in the street outside my apartment. Piccadilly is a busy street. I often look down at the people in Piccadilly.

One Tuesday morning, last year, I was in my sitting-room. It was a sunny morning in early September. I was reading a newspaper. On the front page, there was some news about a horrible murder.

# THE TIMES

*Tuesday, 5th September, 1860*

## HORRIBLE MURDER IN WEST LONDON

◆

YESTERDAY, somebody murdered a man in West London. The murderer killed his victim with a knife.

At three o'clock, somebody heard screams. Then a policeman found the victim's body. The dead man was lying in his own bedroom. There was a knife in the dead man's back, below his neck.

Many policemen are trying to find the murderer.

For ten minutes, I sat and I read about the murder. Then a very strange thing happened. I looked up. For a minute, I was in a different room. Where was I? I was not in my sitting-room. I was in a small dark room in an old house. I was in the victim's bedroom! The murdered man was not there. But I saw his bed. And I saw the blood on his bed! I saw a knife on the bed! I closed my eyes. I was breathing fast. Then I opened my eyes and I was in my sitting-room again.

'What is happening to me?' I asked myself. Quickly, I got up from my chair and I went to the window. I looked down into the street.

Piccadilly was very busy that morning. Many people were walking in the street. Some people were talking to each other. Some people were looking into the shop windows. Three men came along the street together. They saw a friend on the other side of the street. The men did not stop walking, but they shouted 'Good morning!' to each other. Soon, they had gone.

Then suddenly, another strange thing happened. I saw two men walking very quickly along Piccadilly. The first man was about one hundred feet in front of the other man.

I watched the two men for half a minute. They were always one hundred feet apart. The two men did not stop. They did not look at the shops. They did not look at the other people in the street.

'The second man is following the first man,' I said to myself. 'Why is he doing that?'

The first man's face was unhappy. Once, he looked behind him. He looked back at the second man. Then he began to walk faster. But the second man walked faster too.

'The first man is very frightened,' I thought. 'Why is he frightened?'

The second man's face was pale. He stared ahead of him – he looked straight in front of him.

'Is the second man walking in his sleep?' I asked myself. 'No! He isn't asleep. It's late in the morning!'

The two men were not looking at the other people in the street. They were walking straight ahead, very quickly. But they never touched the other people. And the other people in the street were not looking at the two men. Could the other people see these two strange men?

Soon, the first man was opposite my window. He looked up and he stared straight at me. His face was terrible! He stopped walking for a second. Then he walked on quickly.

'Yes, that man is very frightened,' I said to myself. 'I will give him a name. He is the Frightened Man!'

A few moments later, the second man was opposite my window. He looked up at me too.

The man stopped walking for a few seconds. He stood still and he looked at me.

'This man's face is very pale,' I said to myself. 'It is the face of a dead man!'

'The first man was the Frightened Man,' I thought. 'This is the Pale Man. The Pale Man is saying, "Remember me! Help me!"'

Why did I think that? I do not know.

Then, the Pale Man started walking again. Soon, the two men had passed my window. They did not come back.

A moment later, John Derrick came into the room.

'Your lunch is in the dining-room, sir,' he said.

———

Three days later, some policemen arrested a man. They arrested him for murder. They took the man to a police station. They accused him of the murder of the man in West London. The accused man was a friend of the victim. I read about this in the newspaper.

Soon, I forgot about the murder. But I did not forget those two men in the street. I did not forget their strange faces. I did not forget the unhappy face of the Frightened Man. And I did not forget the staring eyes of the Pale Man.

Two months later, I saw both those men again!

## 2

# The Man in the Dressing-room

Now I must tell you more about my apartment.

My bedroom is at the front of the building, between the sitting-room and the dressing-room. I can go into the sitting-room from the corridor of the apartment. And I can go into the bedroom from the corridor. But I cannot go into the dressing-room from the corridor. I have to go into the dressing-room from the bedroom. Here is a plan of my apartment.

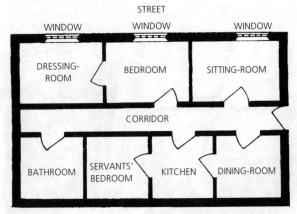

One evening in November, I was standing in my bedroom. It was very dark outside. In the bedroom, two candles were burning.

That evening, I was very tired and I wanted to go to bed early. I went into the dressing-room. I took off my jacket and my tie. Then I returned to the bedroom. I closed the dressing-room door.

43

A moment later, my servant, John Derrick, came into the bedroom.

'I must go out early tomorrow, John,' I said. 'I am going to meet an important person at the bank at half past nine. I will eat my breakfast at half past seven.'

Suddenly, I heard a noise behind John Derrick. The dressing-room door opened. I saw a man standing in the dressing-room. He was staring at me. He waved his hand at me. He did not speak. But he was telling me something. He was saying, 'Come in here!'

I had seen this strange man before. I had seen him in Piccadilly. He was the man with the staring eyes – the Pale Man! Why was he in my dressing-room?

For a moment, I could not move. Then the Pale Man closed the dressing-room door. I took a candle from my table. I ran to the door and I opened it. I went into the dressing-room. But the room was empty! Nobody was there!

John Derrick came into the dressing-room. He looked at my face.

'Sir, what is wrong?' he asked. 'Is somebody here?'

John Derrick had not seen the door open. He had not seen the Pale Man. The door and the man had been behind my servant.

'John, I saw a very strange thing,' I said.

I touched his shoulder. Suddenly, his arm shook.

'Yes, sir,' he said, 'you saw a strange thing. You saw a dead man – a man with a pale face. He was calling you!'

I walked slowly back to the bedroom and I sat on the bed. I was frightened. At first, John had not known about the man in the dressing-room. Then I had touched John's arm. And after that, he had known about the Pale Man.

I was frightened, and John was frightened too. He brought me a glass of brandy. I drank it quickly. But I did not sleep well that night.

———

The next morning, John brought my breakfast at half past seven. He left the dining-room, and he returned a moment later. He brought me a letter.

'I will read the letter this evening, John,' I said. 'I

must go out early this morning. I will be very busy today.'

I was busy all day. In the morning, I went to the bank. There was a lot of work for me at the bank.

In the evening, I went home to my apartment. I opened my letter. The letter was from the Law Courts.

**THE LAW COURTS**

THE OLD BAILEY

NEWGATE STREET, LONDON

18th November
1860

Dear Mr Fotherley

You must come to the Old Bailey law courts on 20th November. You will be a member of the jury in a trial.

You must bring some clothes with you. Some trials go on for many days. The members of the jury in these long trials must not go home at night. The members of the jury have to stay together at an inn.

Please come to the Old Bailey at ten o'clock in the morning. Tell your name to the policeman near the door.

'The twentieth of November! That is tomorrow,' I thought.

I told John about the letter. Quickly, he put some of my clothes into a case. Then I went to bed.

———

The next morning, I got up early. I left the apartment. I walked along Piccadilly. I got into a hansom cab and I went to Newgate Street. At ten o'clock, I arrived at the Old Bailey.

47

## 3

# The Foreman of the Jury

At ten o'clock, I walked into the Old Bailey law courts. There was a policeman near the door of the famous building.

'Good morning, sir!' the policeman said.

I told him my name. He wrote my name on a list.

There are many courtrooms at the Old Bailey. On that day, there was a different trial in each courtroom. There was a list of trials on the wall, near the door. I started to read the list.

Soon, I had a surprise. In one courtroom, there was going to be a trial for murder. A man had been accused of the murder of his friend. The murderer had killed the victim with a knife.

I had read about this murder in the newspaper. I remembered that September day. First, I had read about the murder in the newspaper. Then I had seen the victim's bedroom and the knife. And then the two strange men had passed my window!

I spoke to another policeman. He pointed at a door.

'You must go in there, sir,' he said.

A few minutes later, I was sitting in a courtroom with nineteen other men. Twelve of us were going to be the members of the jury in the murder trial.

Two lawyers were sitting near the front of the court-room. We waited for the judge and the accused man.

A door opened. A policeman brought the accused man into the courtroom.

I looked at the accused man and I had another surprise. I had seen the man before. I had seen him in September. I had seen him on the day after the murder. He was the Frightened Man!

Then another door opened and the judge came into the courtroom. Everybody stood up. I looked at the judge. He was an old man. He was wearing a red robe. He sat down. Then everybody sat down.

The judge spoke to the accused man.

'You are accused of murder,' he said. 'Are you Guilty or Not Guilty?'

'I am Not Guilty, sir,' replied the accused man.

'We will choose the members of the jury,' he said.

He read a name from a list.

'Mr Rodney Black,' he said.

A man near me stood up. 'Yes, sir,' he said.

'Do you know the accused man?' asked the judge.

'No, sir,' said Mr Black.

'Will you try to find the truth about this crime?' asked the judge.

'Yes, sir,' said Mr Black.

'You will be a member of this jury, Mr Black,' said the judge.

Then the judge read another name from his list. He asked another man these questions.

My name was the sixth name on the judge's list.

'Mr George Fotherley,' said the judge.

I stood up and said, 'Yes, sir.'

Suddenly, the accused man started to shout.

'No! He must not be a member of the jury,' the man shouted. 'This will not be a fair trial!'

'Do you know the accused man, Mr Fotherley?' the judge asked me.

'No, sir,' I said. 'I do not know him.'

'Do you know Mr Fotherley?' the judge asked the accused man.

'No, sir,' said the man quietly.

'But you do not like Mr Fotherley?' asked the judge.

'I – I don't know, sir,' said the accused man.

The accused man's lawyer – the lawyer for the defence – stood up. He went to the accused man and spoke to him quietly for a few minutes.

The accused man was frightened. But he did not say anything to the lawyer. The lawyer sat down.

'Do you want to say something?' the judge asked the accused man.

'No, sir,' said the accused man.

'Mr Fotherley,' said the judge. 'Will you try to find the truth about this crime?'

'Yes, sir,' I replied.

'You will be a member of this jury,' said the judge.

Soon, the judge had chosen the twelve members of the jury. The other eight men went away to another courtroom.

'Who will be the foreman of this jury?' asked the judge. 'The foreman will speak for all the members of the jury. You, the jury, will have questions about the trial. The foreman will ask me these questions. He will tell me about your problems. He will ask the other members of the jury about the trial.'

'At the end of the trial, the jury will make their decision,' said the judge. 'The foreman will tell me the jury's decision. He will say, "The accused man is Guilty." Or he will say, "The accused man is *Not* Guilty." Who will be the foreman?'

I did not want to be the foreman of the jury. Nobody wanted to be the foreman. For a moment, nobody spoke. Then my right arm started moving. Was somebody pushing my arm? I looked around me. Nobody was touching me.

Suddenly I said, 'I will be the foreman, sir.'

Why did I say that? I do not know.

'Thank you, Mr Fotherley,' said the judge.

Then the judge spoke to all of us again.

'Members of the jury,' he said. 'This trial is going to be a long trial. It will go on for eleven days. There is a lot of evidence, and there are many witnesses. The witnesses will give their evidence. Some witnesses will tell us about the dead man – the victim. Some witnesses will tell us about the accused man. And some witnesses tell us about the murdered man's bedroom and the knife. All this will be evidence.'

'On the last two days of the trial,' the judge said, 'the lawyers will not talk to the witnesses. They will talk to you, the jury. They will talk about the evidence. Then the lawyer for the prosecution will say, "This man killed his friend. This man is Guilty." The lawyer for the defence will say, "No, this man did *not* kill his friend. This man is Not Guilty." You must listen carefully to the lawyers.'

'Then *I* will talk to you,' said the judge. 'I will talk to you about all the evidence. After that, you will make your decision. You will ask yourselves, "Is the accused man Guilty or is the accused man Not Guilty? Did he murder his friend, or did he *not* murder his friend?" And you will make your decision.'

'The trial will begin now,' said the judge. 'Members of the jury, please listen carefully to all the evidence.'

———

I had some more surprises on that first day of the trial. I was sitting with the other members of the jury and I was listening to the evidence. The lawyer for the prosecution was telling us about the murder. And he was asking a policeman some questions about the victim's body.

'I found the body, sir,' said the policeman. 'The murderer had pushed a knife into the victim's back. The knife was six inches below the victim's neck.'

I listened to the policeman and I looked around me. I looked quickly at the jury.

'There are *thirteen* members of this jury!' I thought.

'There is another person here!'

But then I counted carefully. And there were twelve of us – not thirteen. This happened twice in the morning. And it happened again in the afternoon.

And twice in the afternoon, I asked myself, 'Why is my arm moving? Is somebody pushing my arm?' But nobody was touching me!

———

At the end of the first day, the judge spoke to the jury again.

'You must not go home until the end of the trial,' he told us. 'You must stay together. You must talk to each other about the trial. But you must not talk to any other people about the trial.'

'Each night, you will go to an inn – the London Tavern,' the judge said. 'There is a large room for you at the inn. You will all sleep there. A policeman will take care of you. His name is Mr Harker. Do not talk to him about the trial. Goodnight, members of the jury.'

# 4

# At the London Tavern

At the London Tavern, Mr Harker took us to a large room. There was a big window at one end of the room. Moonlight shone into the room through the window.

There were twelve beds for the jury. Near the door, there was another bed. That bed was for Mr Harker. The policeman put his bed in front of the door.

'I will sleep here,' he said. 'Nobody will leave this room until the morning.'

———

On the second day of the trial, the lawyer for the prosecution told us about the victim.

That evening, the other members of the jury went to sleep quickly. But I was not tired. I could not sleep. I got up and I walked towards Mr Harker. He was sitting on his bed and he was reading quietly.

'Please sit down, Mr Fotherley,' the policeman said.

Mr Harker talked to me for a long time. He was a very interesting old man. He knew about many murder trials. We talked about famous murderers. Soon, it was midnight.

'I must go to sleep now,' I said. I touched Mr Harker on the arm. 'Goodnight.'

Suddenly, the policeman's body shook.

'I am very cold,' said Mr Harker. 'You touched me. And suddenly, I was very cold. Why?'

Then Mr Harker looked towards the window.

'Who is that, Mr Fotherley?' he said quietly. 'All the other men are asleep.'

I saw something next to the window. What was it? It was the figure of a man! He was the Pale Man from Piccadilly – the man with the staring eyes!

The figure walked from one bed to another. He stopped for a moment near each bed. He looked down at the sleeping man in the bed, then he walked to the next bed.

At last, the figure moved back to the window and suddenly he disappeared!

I walked back to my own bed, but I did not sleep well that night.

The next morning, Mr Black said, 'I had a strange dream last night. I dreamt about the murdered man. He wanted to tell me something.'

'I had that dream too!' said another member of the jury.

All the other members of the jury had dreamt about the murdered man. But I had not dreamt about him. And Mr Harker had not dreamt about him. But we had seen a strange figure. Had we seen a ghost?

———

On the third and fourth days of the trial, the jury heard more evidence. Each evening, at the inn, we talked about the trial.

On the evening of the fourth day, we were sitting in our room at the London Tavern.

'The accused man is the murderer,' I said.

Eight members of the jury agreed with me. But the other three men did not agree. They were stupid. They had made their decision on the first day. Their decision was – Not Guilty! They had not listened to the evidence. They were not going to listen to it. They said many stupid things.

Suddenly, I saw the Pale Man. He was standing near the window and he was looking at me. He pointed to the three stupid men. He looked at me again then he disappeared.

I tried to talk to the three stupid men. But they did not listen to me.

'The accused man is Not Guilty,' they said.

# 5

## The Ghost at the Trial

On the fifth day of the trial, the lawyer for the prosecution brought a small picture into the courtroom. It was a picture of the victim.

'This good, kind man was murdered by his friend,' said the lawyer. He brought the picture to the jury. 'Please look at the victim,' he said. '*You* must be his friends now.'

The lawyer gave the picture to me. It was a picture of the Pale Man! Was I surprised? No, I was not! But I knew something. I had seen a ghost!

—

That night, I could not sleep. I lay in my bed at the London Tavern. I thought about ghosts.

I thought about the two strange men in Piccadilly. What were they? Were both of them ghosts?

On that day in September, the Pale Man was dead. But I had seen him in the street. Yes, I had seen him following the Frightened Man. Was the ghost of the victim following the ghost of his murderer? No! On that day in September, the accused man was not a ghost. He was alive! Can a living man have a ghost?

I asked myself a question. 'Did anybody in Piccadilly see those two men?'

And I knew the answer. 'No! I saw them through my window. But nobody in the street saw them!'

'The two men looked up at my window,' I thought. 'The Frightened Man looked up, and he was afraid of me. The Pale Man looked up, and he stared at me. He was saying, "Remember me! Please remember me! Please help me!" I must help him! I *will* help him!'

———

The next day was the sixth day of the trial. The lawyer for the defence started to talk to us. For the next four days, the lawyer for the defence spoke to his witnesses. He asked them about the accused man.

One witness said, 'He is a good kind man. He did not kill his friend.'

Then the lawyer asked the witness about the victim. The witness said, 'He was a wicked man. He did bad things.'

———

On the seventh day of the trial, I saw the Pale Man in the courtroom for the first time.

Was he in the courtroom on the first six days of the trial? Yes, he was. He pushed my arm. The Pale Man sat with the jury. He was the thirteenth man. He was there. But I did not see him clearly. But, then on the seventh day, I saw him very clearly in the courtroom!

A witness was telling the lawyer for the defence about the dead man. The witness was a friend of the accused man.

'The murdered man was a bad man,' the witness said. 'Many people wanted to kill him. But my friend did *not* want to kill him. He wanted to help him.'

Suddenly, the ghost of the victim was standing next to the witness. The ghost moved his head sadly. The witness could not see him. The lawyers could not see him. The judge could not see him and the other members of the jury could not see him. But I could see him!

After that, I saw the Pale Man in the courtroom every day. He stood next to the witnesses for the defence. They spoke and he moved his head sadly.

Sometimes the judge wrote down the witnesses' words. Then the Pale Man stood next to the judge's chair and he looked at the writing. He read the writing and he moved his head sadly.

None of these people could see the ghost. The witnesses could not see the ghost. But he stood next to them. And suddenly, they stopped speaking. The judge could not see the ghost. But the ghost stood next to him and the judge stopped writing. I could see the ghost. He was telling me, 'These witnesses are lying! Do not believe them!'

—

On the tenth day of the trial, the defence lawyer made his final speech. It was late in the afternoon. The lawyer pointed to the accused man.

'This man is not a murderer,' the lawyer said. 'He is a good man. Nobody killed his friend – the man killed himself. He killed himself with his own knife.'

The lawyer spoke these words loudly. The members of the jury were surprised. The judge was surprised. The lawyer for the prosecution was surprised.

And the ghost was surprised! The Pale Man stood next to the lawyer for the defence. He moved his head. Then he moved his left arm behind his back. And he moved his right arm behind his back.

The Pale Man looked at me. He was telling me something again. He was saying, 'It is not possible. I could not kill myself with my right hand. And I could not kill myself with my left hand.' And this was true!

On the eleventh day, the judge spoke to the jury. He told us again about the murder. He told us about the accused man and about the victim. He told us about the witnesses.

'The witnesses say many different things,' said the judge. 'They do not agree with each other. You, the jury, must make your decision. Who is telling the truth? Which witnesses do you believe? You must make your decision. Then you must tell me that decision.'

'But it is late now,' the judge said. 'Members of the jury, you must go to the London Tavern for one more night. You must tell me your decision tomorrow morning. Is the accused man Guilty, or Not Guilty? Tomorrow we will know. Goodnight, members of the jury.'

———

That evening, we talked about our decision. Nine of us said, 'The accused man is Guilty. He killed his friend.' But three men – the three stupid men – did not believe us, 'No!' they said. 'The man killed himself.'

Suddenly, I saw the Pale Man by the window. He pointed at me.

'No, the victim did not kill himself,' I said angrily.

I moved my arms behind me. I had seen the ghost doing this. 'Look!' I said. 'It is not possible.'

We talked for an hour. At last, the three stupid men agreed with me. 'The accused man is Guilty,' they said.

———

The next morning, the judge came into the courtroom and he sat down. Suddenly, the Pale Man was standing beside him. Then the accused man came in. The ghost looked at him and he looked at the jury. Next, he looked straight at me. He pointed at me. Then he pointed at the accused man and he pointed at himself.

The judge spoke to me.

'Foreman of the jury,' he said. 'Has the jury made a decision? Is the accused man Guilty or Not Guilty?'

'He is Guilty,' I said. And at that moment, the ghost disappeared!

'Thank you, members of the jury,' the judge said.

Then he spoke to the guilty man.

'You are guilty of murder,' the judge said. 'You will die. You will be hanged with a rope.'

'This trial was not fair!' the murderer shouted.

Then the murderer pointed at me.

'I had a dream about that man,' he shouted. 'I had never met him. But in my dream, that man was putting a rope round my neck!'

The murderer was screaming. Quickly, two policemen took him away. Then everybody stood up and left the courtroom. I did not leave.

I sat in the courtroom for a few minutes. I was tired. Suddenly, somebody put his hand on my arm. I looked round, but there was nobody there. I was alone.

Published by Macmillan Heinemann ELT
Between Towns Road, Oxford OX4 3PP
Macmillan Heinemann ELT is an imprint of
Macmillan Publishers Limited
Companies and representatives throughout the world
Heinemann is a registered trademark of Harcourt Education, used under licence.

ISBN 1–405072–49–0
EAN 978–1–405072–49–6

This retold version by F. H. Cornish for Macmillan Readers
First published 1998
Text © F. H. Cornish 1998, 2005
Design and illustration © Macmillan Publishers Limited 1998, 2005

This edition first published 2005

Designed by Sue Vaudin
Illustrated by Paul Fisher-Johnson
Map on page 3 and illustrations on pages 6–8 by John Gilkes
Typography by Adrian Hodgkins
Original cover template design by Jackie Hill
Cover illustration: 'On the Pont de L'Europe' by Gustave Caillebotte/
Kimbell Art Museum/Corbis

Printed in Thailand

2009  2008  2007  2006
10  9  8  7  6  5  4  3  2